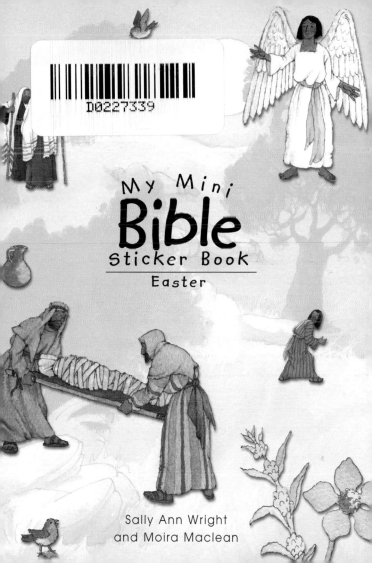

D0227339

My Mini
Bible
Sticker Book
Easter

Sally Ann Wright
and Moira Maclean

The king on a donkey

Jesus healed people with terrible diseases. He calmed a storm and made sure hungry people had enough to eat. He showed everyone how much God loved them.

One day, Jesus and his friends went to Jerusalem to celebrate the Passover feast.

2

Jesus rode on a donkey. As he approached the city gates, people were waiting. They couldn't wait to greet him!

Some cut down palm branches and waved them. Others put their cloaks in front of the donkey to make a soft path.

'Hooray for Jesus!' they shouted. 'Here comes our king!'

The last supper

Jesus decided to eat the Passover meal with his special friends in the upstairs room of a house.

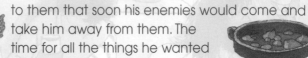

   As they sat around the table together, Jesus explained to them that soon his enemies would come and take him away from them. The time for all the things he wanted

to tell them had come to an end. This would be the last time they ate together for a while.

While Jesus was speaking, one of his friends crept out into the night. He had been paid thirty silver coins to tell the soldiers where to find Jesus. The friend's name was Judas.

Jesus prays in the garden

After supper, they all went on to a hillside nearby covered with olive trees. It was called the Garden of Gethsemane.

The men were all tired. But Jesus asked his friends to stay with him while he prayed.

Jesus knew that terrible things would soon happen to him. He asked God to help him

to be brave enough.

When Jesus went back to his friends, they had all fallen asleep. Jesus asked them to wait with him while he prayed again.

But already the soldiers were coming. Judas had betrayed his friend.

Pontius Pilate and the angry crowd

Jesus was arrested by the soldiers. His friends ran away and left him. Jesus was marched away to see the Roman governor.

Pontius Pilate was not angry with Jesus. He knew Jesus had done nothing wrong. But outside his window there was an angry crowd.

'Crucify Jesus!' the angry men shouted. 'Put him on a cross to die!'

Where were the people Jesus had helped? Where were all his friends now?

In the crowd were men who were jealous of Jesus. These men paid others to shout and ask for Jesus to be put to death. Their cruel plan was working.

A cross between two thieves

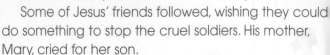

Jesus was taken away to a hill called Calvary.

Some of Jesus' friends followed, wishing they could do something to stop the cruel soldiers. His mother, Mary, cried for her son.

Jesus was put on a cross between two thieves. He was in terrible pain but he called down to his

riend John. He asked him to look after his mother
as if she was his own mother. Then he asked Mary
to treat John as if he were her own son.
John and Mary were frightened and
sad. They knew that Jesus would die
before the day was ended.

The miracle of the resurrection

Jesus died later that afternoon. Some friends took down his body from the cross and buried it in a cave. Jesus' friend Mary Magdalene watched as they rolled a big stone in front of it.

On Sunday morning Mary went into the garden with a jar of perfume. She hoped

o anoint Jesus' body. But what had happened? omeone had moved the stone. And two angels vere there!

'Jesus isn't here,' they told her. 'God has raised im from the dead. Jesus is alive!'

Mary was amazed! Could this be true? Could her friend ave been dead but now be alive again?

13

Mary meets Jesus

Mary turned away from the angels, not sure what
to do next. She still didn't understand what the
angels could mean. Then Mary saw a man standing
in the garden.

'Please,' she said, thinking it was the gardener,
'do you know where they have taken Jesus?'

The man did not answer her question. He just spoke her name.

'Mary!' he said. And suddenly Mary knew who it was! This really was Jesus, once dead and now alive!

'Go and tell my friends so that they can be happy too!' Jesus said. So Mary ran to tell everyone the good news that Jesus was very much alive.

Copyright © 2012 Anno Domini Publishing
www.ad-publishing.com

Text copyright © 2005 Sally Ann Wright
Illustrations copyright © 2005 Moira Maclean

All rights reserved

Editorial Director: Annette Reynolds
Art Director: Gerald Rogers
Pre-production Manager: Krystyna Hewitt
Production Manager: John Laister

Published 2014 by Authentic Media Ltd
52 Presley Way, Crownhill, Milton Keynes,
MK8 0ES, UK

Conforms to EN71

Printed and bound in China